PINK FLOYD TRIVIA BOOK

Uncover The Facts of One of The
Greatest Bands
in Rock N Roll History!

By Dale Raynes

Please consider writing a review!

Just visit: purplelink.org/review

Bridge Press.

bp@purplelink.org

ISBN: 978-1-955149-06-8

TABLE OF CONTENTS

Introduction 1

Chapter 1: Origins and Early Years 3
Trivia Time! 3
Answers 7
Did You Know? 9

Chapter 2: Early Albums 11
Trivia Time! 11
Answers 15
Did You Know? 17

Chapter 3: Growing Fame 19
Trivia Time! 19
Answers 24
Did You Know? 26

Chapter 4: Superstardom 28
Trivia Time! 28
Answers 32

Did You Know? 34

Chapter 5: Later Albums 36

Trivia Time! 36

Answers 40

Did You Know? 42

Chapter 6: Key People.. 44

Trivia Time! 44

Answers 48

Did You Know? 49

Chapter 7: Songs of the Early Years 51

Trivia Time! 51

Answers 56

Did You Know? 58

Chapter 8: Songs of Later Years 60

Trivia Time! 60

Answers 64

Did You Know? 65

Chapter 9: Live Performances and Tours 67

Trivia Time! 67

Answers 71

Did You Know? 73

Chapter 10: Movies, Television, and Videos 75

Trivia Time! 75

Answers... 80

Did You Know? 82

Chapter 11: Solo and Side Projects 84

Trivia Time! 84

Answers... 89

Did You Know? 91

Chapter 12: Honors and Awards 93

Trivia Time! 93

Answers... 98

Did You Know? 100

Chapter 13: Influence, Legacy, and Miscellany .. 102

Trivia Time! 102

Answers... 106

Did You Know? 107

INTRODUCTION

Pink Floyd's music has resonated with listeners of all ages on a deep personal level for more than half a century. They were one of the most prominent British rock bands to achieve worldwide fame after the initial "British Invasion" led by The Beatles and The Rolling Stones in the early 1960s. Founded in 1965, the band reached the height of its popularity and influence in the 1970s and early '80s. Pink Floyd is one of the most commercially successful bands of all time, with an estimated 250 million albums sold, and the band remains highly influential among fellow musicians.

Pink Floyd members David Gilmour, Roger Waters, Nick Mason, Rick Wright, and Syd Barrett were inducted into the Rock & Roll Hall of Fame in 1996. "Pink Floyd were the architects of two major music movements—psychedelic space-rock and blues-based progressive rock—and became known for their biting political, social, and emotional commentary," the Hall of Fame's website states. "With 1973's *Dark Side of The Moon* and 1979's *The Wall*, the band created two of the most ambitious (and best-selling) albums of all time—and underscored that personal torment could resonate on a massive level."

To help you connect, or perhaps reconnect, with the lives, music, and legacy of this fascinating band, interesting facts and historical moments are highlighted in this book, *Pink Floyd:*

1

Trivia Book.

We will cover the history of Pink Floyd, beginning with the origins of the band, through changes in personnel and musical philosophy, up to their influence and reputation today. A series of multiple choice and true/false questions opens each chapter, with the corresponding answers on the following page. The "Did You Know?" section consists of interesting facts and stories, which close each chapter so that you can develop a stronger understanding of the life and music of Pink Floyd.

The information in this book is up to date as of early 2021. Because the band has not recorded new material since the release of *The Endless River* in 2014, the historical facts should remain mostly consistent. Records and stats may fluctuate with future anniversary releases.

Use this book to test your knowledge with a round of trivia questions and perhaps review or gain information along the way. Whether you consider yourself a die-hard fan or are only faintly familiar with Pink Floyd, this book offers the opportunity to reinforce your knowledge of one of the most innovative and influential bands in the history of popular music.

Let's see how much you know about Pink Floyd!

CHAPTER 1:

ORIGINS AND EARLY YEARS

TRIVIA TIME!

1. Which future member of Pink Floyd was taught by Roger Waters' mother, Mary, in junior high school?

   a. Nick Mason
   b. Rick Wright
   c. Syd Barrett
   d. David Gilmour

2. True or False: Roger Waters and Syd Barrett were classmates and roommates while studying architecture at the London Polytechnic.

3. Which of the following "British Invasion" bands did the new band cover during their earliest performances in 1963?

   a. Gerry and the Pacemakers
   b. The Searchers
   c. Herman's Hermits
   d. The Hollies

4. Which of the following was <u>not</u> one of the names of the band that Roger Waters, Keith Noble, and Rick Wright were members of from 1963 to 1965?

   a. The Wranglers

b. The Abdabs

c. Sigma 6

d. Tea Set

5. Which instrument did Rick Wright play in the earliest iteration of the band?

a. Saxophone

b. Rhythm guitar

c. Keyboards

d. Percussion

6. True or False: Roger Waters originally played lead guitar in the band before switching to bass guitar.

7. In which British city was the band based?

a. Glasgow

b. Liverpool

c. London

d. Manchester

8. What was the name of the club where the band had its first London show and residency?

a. The Kit Kat Club

b. The Cavern Club

c. The Countdown Club

d. Preservation Hall

9. True or False: Guitarist Bob Klose quit the band because he couldn't get along with Syd Barrett.

10. Which of these musicians was not a member when the band changed its name to The Pink Floyd Sound?

a. Syd Barrett

b. David Gilmour

c. Nick Mason

d. Roger Waters

e. Rick Wright

11. True or False: Syd Barrett thought of the name "Pink Floyd" from two blues musicians who were in his record collection, Pink Anderson and Floyd Council.

12. Which of the following elements was <u>not</u> characteristic of the band's evolving sound from 1965 through 1967?

a. Long instrumental solos

b. Improvisation and atonality

c. Experiments with "psychedelic" lighting

d. A polished, upbeat pop vibe

13. True or False: Singer Chris Dennis quit the band to join a Buddhist monastery in Tibet.

14. Which of these was <u>not</u> one of the venues Pink Floyd played as their popularity grew in 1966 and 1967?

a. Wembley Stadium

b. The Countdown Club

c. The Marquee Club

d. The UFO Club

15. In early 1967, Pink Floyd signed with which major record label?

a. RCA

b. Atlantic

c. Capitol

d. EMI

16. Where in London did Pink Floyd's first official recording session take place, not including sessions held before they

adopted that name?

a. Cambridge
b. West Hampstead
c. Covent Garden
d. Soho

17. True or False: Pink Floyd's first single, "Arnold Layne," was banned by London Radio because of it refers to cross-dressing and underwear.

18. What is the title of Pink Floyd's second single, released in June 1967?

a. "See Emily Play"
b. "See Spot Run"
c. "Go Cat Go"
d. "Johnny B. Goode"

19. True or False: Pink Floyd's first appearance on the popular BBC television show *Top of the Pops* was so poorly received that they were not invited back.

20. Which member's erratic behavior became a serious concern for his bandmates as Pink Floyd's fame grew throughout 1967?

a. Nick Mason
b. Roger Waters
c. Syd Barrett
d. Rick Wright

ANSWERS

1. c—Syd Barrett

2. False—Roger Waters was a classmate and roommate of Nick Mason (not Syd Barrett) at the London Polytechnic. However, Waters and Barrett attended the same junior high and high school.

3. b—The Searchers

4. a—The Wranglers

5. b—Rhythm guitar

6. True—Waters switched to bass when Bob Klose joined the band in 1964.

7. c—London

8. c—The Countdown Club

9. False—Klose quit the band because his parents and his college tutors convinced him that he should focus on his studies.

10. b—David Gilmour

11. True—Barrett said he thought of those two musicians more or less randomly.

12. d—A polished, upbeat pop vibe. (The band was moving away from typical pop songs.)

13. False—Chris Dennis left the band to accept a post with the Royal Air Force in Bahrain.

14. a—Wembley Stadium

15. d—EMI/Columbia

16. b—West Hampstead

17. True

18. a—"See Emily Play"

19. False—Pink Floyd was invited back two more times in quick succession.

20. c—Syd Barrett

DID YOU KNOW?

- In 1964, Metcalfe and Noble left to form their own band, and guitarist Syd Barrett joined the group. Singer Chris Dennis also joined the group around the same time, but he soon left to accept a post with the Royal Air Force in Bahrain. Dennis later said, "My only regret was I wish I'd taken more photographs of the guys back then."

- Pink Floyd's sets gradually featured more of Barrett's original compositions and fewer cover songs. Live performances included extended improvisational jams, atonality, and wild antics by Barrett. After a gig at a Catholic youth club, the owner refused to pay them, saying that their performance was not music. Nonetheless, Pink Floyd was steadily building a loyal audience, especially at the UFO Club in London.

- Pink Floyd was known for their stretched-out versions of songs, especially in the Syd Barrett era. However, band members admit that this was more a question of necessity than innovative brilliance. When the band got its first regular gig at the Countdown Club near Kensington High Street in London, they were required to play three sets of 90 minutes every night. According to Nick Mason, the band soon learned that "songs could be extended with lengthy solos" in order to fill up the time.

- The band also began experimenting with instrumental improvisations and "psychedelic" light shows in its early shows. At first, this was also an attempt to distract from the material, which consisted mainly of covers. "There wasn't anything grand about it," Roger Waters later said. "We were laughable. We were useless. We couldn't play at all, so we had to do something stupid and 'experimental.'" However, within a year they had matured into one of the most remarkable psychedelic bands of all time.

- By 1967 Pink Floyd was ready for prime time. The four band members entered an agreement with business managers Peter Jenner and Andrew King, whereby each man owned a one-sixth share of the group. After signing with EMI, the band condensed their brilliance into a series of innovative singles such as "See Emily Play" and "Apples and Oranges."

CHAPTER 2:

EARLY ALBUMS

TRIVIA TIME!

1. What was the title of Pink Floyd's first album, released in August 1967?

   a. *The Pied Piper*
   b. *The Piper at the Gates of Dawn*
   c. *The Pearly Gates*
   d. *Gates of Heaven*

2. Who wrote most of the songs on the group's debut album?

   a. Rick Wright
   b. Roger Waters
   c. Syd Barrett
   d. Nick Mason

3. True or False: Pink Floyd's first album reached the Top 10 in the UK.

4. Which prestigious music festival did Pink Floyd have to miss due to Syd Barrett's increasing unreliability?

   a. National Jazz and Blues Festival
   b. Isle of Wight Festival
   c. Glastonbury Festival
   d. Reading Festival

5. Which of these TV music shows did Pink Floyd appear on

during their first US tour?

a. *The Midnight Special*
b. *Soul Train*
c. *Austin City Limits*
d. *American Bandstand*

6. Which musician did Pink Floyd open for during his/her British tour in 1967?

   a. Frank Sinatra
   b. Elvis Presley
   c. Jimi Hendrix
   d. Janis Joplin

7. Which member of Pink Floyd invited David Gilmour to join the band?

   a. Syd Barrett
   b. Nick Mason
   c. Roger Waters
   d. Rick Wright

8. True or False: Soon before leaving Pink Floyd, Syd Barrett introduced a song called "Have You Got It Yet?," which his bandmates found impossible to learn.

9. With Syd Barrett's departure from the band, which member of Pink Floyd eventually became responsible for the overall creative direction?

   a. Roger Waters
   b. Rick Wright
   c. David Gilmour
   d. Nick Mason

10. True or False: Business managers Peter Jenner and Andrew King remained with Pink Floyd after Syd Barrett left the

band in early 1968.

11. True or False: When Pink Floyd appeared on TV immediately after Syd Barrett's departure, David Gilmour lip-synched to recordings of Barrett's voice.

12. What was the title of Pink Floyd's second album, released in June 1968?

    a. *Flying Saucers*
    b. *The Secret Garden*
    c. *Secret World*
    d. *A Saucerful of Secrets*

13. Which song written by Syd Barrett was the last one that Pink Floyd recorded while he was still in the band?

    a. "Jazzman"
    b. "Jugband Blues"
    c. "Birmingham Blues"
    d. "Jughead Jones"

14. True or False: During the recording of Pink Floyd's second album, producer Norman Smith said, "You can't do twenty minutes of this ridiculous noise."

15. What was the name of the design group that developed the cover art for *A Saucerful of Secrets* and several other Pink Floyd albums?

    a. Hipnotism
    b. Hypnotique
    c. Hipgnosis
    d. Genosis

16. Which of the following is not a song written by Roger Waters that was included on the album *A Saucerful of*

Secrets?

    a. "Set the Controls for the Heart of the Sun"
    b. "Corporal Clegg"
    c. "Let There Be More Light"
    d. "The Dawning Sky"

17. True or False: *A Saucerful of Secrets* outperformed Pink Floyd's first album, *The Piper at the Gates of Dawn*, on the UK charts.

18. Who is credited as songwriter of the title track on *A Saucerful of Secrets*?

    a. Roger Waters
    b. Rick Wright
    c. Nick Mason
    d. David Gilmour
    e. All of the above

19. True or False: On the day *A Saucerful of Secrets* was released, Pink Floyd performed at the first-ever free concert in London's Hyde Park.

ANSWERS

1. b—*The Piper at the Gates of Dawn*

2. c—Syd Barrett wrote or co-wrote 10 of the 11 songs on the album.

3. True—*The Piper at the Gates of Dawn* peaked at No. 6 in the UK.

4. a—National Jazz and Blues Festival

5. d—"American Bandstand"

6. c—Jimi Hendrix

7. b—Nick Mason

8. True

9. a—Roger Waters

10. False—Jenner and King decided to stick with Barrett, believing him to have a brighter future than Pink Floyd.

11. False. Roger Waters lip-synched Barrett's parts. While Gilmour vaguely mimed background vocals.

12. d—*A Saucerful of Secrets*

13. b—"Jugband Blues"

14. True—The band was constantly moving away from typical pop-style song construction.

15. c—Hipgnosis

16. d—"The Dawning Sky"

17. False—*A Saucerful of Secrets* peaked at No. 9 on the UK charts while *The Piper at the Gates of Dawn* reached No. 6.

18. e—All of the above

19. True

DID YOU KNOW?

- Pink Floyd's booking agent, Bryan Morrison, negotiated the band's first recording contract with EMI-Columbia. Pink Floyd's first album, The Piper at the Gates of Dawn, was recorded at Abbey Road Studios in London, produced by Norman Smith, and released in August 1967.

- The Piper at the Gates of Dawn spent 14 weeks on the UK charts and peaked at No. 6. It was released in the US on the Tower Records label. Though it did not break any sales records at the time, it has since been recognized as an absolute classic. For example, Mojo magazine ranks it No. 77 amongst the greatest albums of all time.

- Barrett's lasting influence derives from his innovative free-form guitar playing and his experimentation with dissonance, distortion, echoes, feedback, and other effects that were revolutionary for the time. His sophisticated yet unorthodox psychedelic song structures were also incredibly influential.

- Pink Floyd's second album, A Saucerful of Secrets, included three songs written by Roger Waters and two by Rick Wright. The title track on the album runs for almost 12 minutes. It is entirely instrumental, except for some vocalizations by David Gilmour and Rick Wright that do not include any recognizable words.

- Pink Floyd embarked on their second visit to the United States in July 1968. It turned out to be a much more extensive tour than the abortive visit the previous year.

CHAPTER 3:

GROWING FAME

TRIVIA TIME!

1. True or False: Pink Floyd's album *More*, the soundtrack to the movie of the same name, includes all the songs that are in the film.

2. Prior to their work on *More*, Pink Floyd recorded original music that was used in the following 1968 movie (but was not released as an album):

   a. *Rosemary's Baby*
   b. *The Committee*
   c. *Barbarella*
   d. *2001: A Space Odyssey*

3. At which venue did Pink Floyd record some of the live performances that were captured on their album *Ummagumma*?

   a. The Marquee Club
   b. Wembley Stadium
   c. College of Commerce
   d. The UFO Club

4. Beginning with *Ummagumma*, the next several Pink Floyd albums were released in the UK by which new label that was spun off by EMI/Columbia to specialize in progressive rock?

a. Dunhill
b. Asylum
c. A&M
d. Harvest

5. True or False: *Ummagumma* was the most successful of Pink Floyd's first four albums in both the UK and the US.

6. Which composer was hired to write the o orchestral arrangements on*Atom Heart Mother*??

a. Ron Geesin
b. Aaron Copland
c. Philip Glass
d. Albert Ayler

7. True or False: Norman Smith produced *Atom Heart Mother,* as well as three of Pink Floyd's four previous albums.

8. True or False: *Atom Heart Mother* was the first Pink Floyd album to reach No. 1 in the UK.

9. Which member of Pink Floyd called *Atom Heart Mother* "a load of rubbish"?

a. Nick Mason
b. Roger Waters
c. Rick Wright
d. David Gilmour

10. Which of the following bands did not play at the famous Bath Festival of Jazz and Progressive Music in June 1970?

a. Jefferson Airplane
b. Led Zeppelin
c. The Rolling Stones

d. Pink Floyd

11. True or False: The Bath Festival marked the first public appearance of David Gilmour's iconic 1969 black Fender Stratocaster.

12. Pink Floyd's sixth album, released in October 1971, has been called a transition between the early "psychedelic" Pink Floyd and the maturing band that was defining "progressive rock." What is the title of this album?

a. Meddle
b. Muddle
c. Medley
d. Middlin'

13. *Obscured by Clouds*, Pink Floyd's seventh album, is based on the band's soundtrack for a film made by the same director that the band worked with on *More* in 1969. What is the name of that director?

a. John Cassavetes
b. Barbet Schroeder
c. John Frankenheimer
d. Michelangelo Antonioni

14. The recording engineer for the classic album *The Dark Side of the Moon* was later a songwriter and frontman for his own band. What is his name?

a. Trevor Rabin
b. Andrew Loog-Oldham
c. David Byrne
d. Alan Parsons

15. True or False: The iconic artwork for the *The Dark Side of the*

Moon album cover was created by Andy Warhol.

16. Which member of Pink Floyd wrote <u>all</u> the lyrics on *The Dark Side of the Moon*, purposefully making them more direct than those of previous songs?

    a. David Gilmour
    b. Nick Mason
    c. Roger Waters
    d. Rick Wright

17. *The Dark Side of the Moon* featured Pink Floyd's first top 20 Billboard single. What is the song's title?

    a. "Time"
    b. "Money"
    c. "Breathe"
    d. "Us and Them"

18. Which of the following is <u>not</u> believed to be a key theme of *The Dark Side of the Moon*?

    a. Love
    b. Greed
    c. Time
    d. Death

19. Which of the following statements about *The Dark Side of the Moon* is <u>not</u> true?

    a. It reached No. 1 in the US and UK.
    b. It remained on the Billboard Top 200 Albums chart for 955 weeks.
    c. It's the second best-selling album of all time globally, with over 50 million units sold.
    d. It was deemed "culturally, historically, or aesthetically

significant" by the United States Library of Congress.

ANSWERS

1. False — There are two Pink Floyd songs, "Hollywood" and "Seabirds," that are in the movie but not on the album.

2. b — *The Committee*

3. c — Manchester College of Commerce and Mothers

4. d — Harvest

5. True — *Ummagumma* spent 21 weeks on the UK charts and peaked at No. 5, and reached No. 74 on the Billboard chart.

6. a — Ron Geesin

7. False — Norman Smith was listed as executive producer, which David Gilmour said was "a neat way of saying he didn't do anything." This album ended Smith's association with the band.

8. True

9. d — David Gilmour

10. c — The Rolling Stones

11. True

12. a — *Meddle*

13. b — Barbet Schroeder

14. d — Alan Parsons

15. False — Like many Pink Floyd album covers, it was designed by the British creative group Hipgnosis (Storm Thorgerson and George Hardie).

16. c — Roger Waters

17. b—"Money"

18. a—Love

19. a—Reached No. 1 in the US and UK. (It peaked at No. 2 in the UK while remaining on the charts for 364 weeks.)

DID YOU KNOW?

- Though forgotten, the soundtrack to the album *More* contains a broad palette of moods. Exciting are the heavier moments, such as the "Nile Song," which play with a proto-metal sound. The band was quite good at it but did not explore further.

- *Ummagumma* was part live album and part solo compositions by each member. While a lot of the solo stuff is an acquired taste, the live part was incredibly well-received at the time. The International Times reviewer described it as "probably one of the best live recordings I have ever heard."

- The song "Alan's Psychedelic Breakfast" was one of the stranger tracks on *Atom Heart Mother*. It featured roadie Alan Styles narrating his breakfast preparation and eating in extensive detail. He can be heard saying things like "Oh... Er... Me flakes... Scrambled eggs, bacon, sausages, tomatoes, toast, coffee... Marmalade, I like marmalade... "A particularly savage review of *Atom Heart Mother* in *Rolling Stone* magazine called it "the only redeeming feature" on the second side.

- Geesin and the band members composed the title track of *Atom Heart Mother*, a six-part suite that lasted 23 minutes and took up one whole side of the album. Roger Waters and Nick Mason had to play their instruments (bass and drums, respectively) in one continuous take for the entire 23 minutes.

- Hardcore fans still love the extended jams and artsy songs on *Atom Heart Mother* and *Ummagumma*. However, the band members have notably treated this period's music as inferior to the string of more successful albums they would release later. David Gilmour called *Ummagumma* "horrible," and Rick Wright referred to his contribution to this album as "pretentious." Waters opined, "If somebody said to me now – right – here's a million pounds, go out and play *Atom Heart Mother*, I'd say you must be fucking joking."

CHAPTER 4:

SUPERSTARDOM

TRIVIA TIME!

1. *Wish You Were Here* was the first Pink Floyd album released in the US by which record label after the band left Capitol Records?

   a. RCA
   b. Columbia
   c. Reprise
   d. Elektra/Asylum

2. Recording engineer Alan Parsons declined to work on *Wish You Were Here*, having started his own band. What was the name of his band?

   a. Ambrosia
   b. Awareness
   c. The Alan Parsons Project
   d. Surrealism

3. True or False: When Syd Barrett came to visit during the recording of *Wish You Were Here*, his former bandmates did not recognize him.

4. Which member of Pink Floyd wrote all the lyrics for *Wish You Were Here*?

   a. David Gilmour

b. Nick Mason

c. Roger Waters

d. Rick Wright

5. True or False: *Wish You Were Here* went straight to No. 1 in the UK and reached No. 1 in the US in its second week after release.

6. Which song was the first single from *Wish You Were Here*?

a. "Have a Cigar"/"Welcome to the Machine"

b. "Shine On You Crazy Diamond"

c. "Us and Them"

d. "Wish You Were Here"

7. In 1976, Pink Floyd recorded their album *Animals* at a property they had recently bought in the Islington district of London. What was the property previously used for?

a. Library

b. Dog kennel

c. Roller rink

d. Part of a church

8. True or False: The concept for *Animals* was inspired by George Orwell's novel *Animal Farm*.

9. Which of the following is not one of the tracks on *Animals*?

a. "Horses"

b. "Dogs"

c. "Sheep"

d. "Pigs On the Wing (part one)"

10. True or False: *Animals* was the first Pink Floyd album with no songwriting credit for Rick Wright.

11. True or False: *Animals* reached No. 1 in both the UK and the

United States.

12. What was the name of Pink Floyd's 1977 North American tour to support *Animals*?

    a. Animal House
    b. In the Flesh
    c. The Barnyard Tour
    d. The Monkey House

13. Which member of Pink Floyd became so annoyed by a group of unruly fans at a concert in Montreal in 1977 that he spat at them?

    a. Nick Mason
    b. David Gilmour
    c. Roger Waters
    d. Rick Wright

14. True or False: Roger Waters said that one of the themes for Pink Floyd's album *The Wall* was the idea of building a wall between the band and its audience.

15. Which of the following songs from *The Wall* was <u>not</u> co-written by Roger Waters and David Gilmour?

    a. "Comfortably Numb"
    b. "The Trial"
    c. "Run Like Hell"
    d. "Young Lust"

16. True or False: Rick Wright was fired after the recording of *The Wall* and never played with Pink Floyd again.

17. Which song from *The Wall* became Pink Floyd's first No. 1 single in both the UK and US?

    a. "Another Brick in the Wall (Part 2)"

b. "Is There Anybody Out There?"
c. "Run Like Hell"
d. "Comfortably Numb"

18. True or False: Like every Pink Floyd album since *The Piper at the Gates of Dawn*, the packaging for *The Wall* was developed by Storm Thorgerson of the design group Hipgnosis.

19. When *The Wall* was later adapted into a film, *Pink Floyd – The Wall*, which musician played the lead role of Pink?

a. Roger Waters
b. David Bowie
c. Bryan Ferry
d. Bob Geldof

ANSWERS

1. b — Columbia

2. c — The Alan Parsons Project

3. True — Barrett had gained a good deal of weight and shaved his head and eyebrows since his friends had last seen him.

4. c — Roger Waters

5. True — Demand was such that retailers were able to receive only 50 percent of their initial orders.

6. a — "Have a Cigar"

7. d — Church meeting hall

8. True

9. a — "Horses"

10. True — Wright later said, "This was when Roger *really* started to believe that he was the sole writer for the band."

11. False — *Animals* peaked at No. 2 in the UK and No. 3 in the US.

12. b — In the Flesh

13. c — Roger Waters. Waters later admitted that the spitting incident was one of the inspirations for Pink Floyd's next album, *The Wall*.

14. True — The idea came to Waters while he was feeling frustrated and alienated during the 1977 world tour.

15. b — "The Trial"

16. False — Wright was dismissed during the recording of album, but he rejoined the band for the subsequent *The Wall* tour (not as a member, but as a salaried player). He rejoined the band full time in 1994.

17. a — "Another Brick in the Wall (Part 2)"

18. False — The design was done by cartoonist and animator Gerald Scarfe, after Waters had a falling out with the designers of all their previous cover work.

19. d — Bob Geldof

DID YOU KNOW?

- After touring extensively to support *The Dark Side of the Moon*, Pink Floyd began work on their ninth studio album, *Wish You Were Here*, in January 1975. The band members were exhausted from the constant touring and the general hysteria surrounding *The Dark Side of the Moon* and were well aware that it would be a tough act to follow. "The girls and the money and the fame and all that stuff," David Gilmour said, "everything had sort of come our way, and you had to reassess what you were in it for thereafter, and it was a pretty confusing and sort of empty time for a while."

- After some false starts, Roger Waters finally came upon a central theme for *Wish You Were Here* — the rise and fall of his friend and former bandmate Syd Barrett. This reportedly happened after Waters heard a random four-note guitar phrase by David Gilmour, which reminded him of Barrett.

- *Wish You Were Here* was released in September 1975 by Harvest in the UK and Columbia in the US, reaching No. 1 on both sides of the Atlantic. While initially regarded as inferior to its predecessor, *Wish You Were Here* has sold over 20 million copies and is now considered one of the greatest albums of all time. Both David Gilmour and Rick Wright have called it their favorite Pink Floyd album.

- Pink Floyd's next project was *The Wall*, a rock opera based on a concept developed by Roger Waters and producer Bob Ezrin. The main character, Pink, was inspired by Waters's own childhood experiences, including his father's death in World War II. As an adult, Pink is a rock star. Various problems and challenges before him are bricks in a metaphorical wall that he eventually resolves to tear down.

- Recording sessions for *The Wall* and the subsequent tour marked a low ebb in interpersonal relationships between the band members. Not only was Rick Wright asked to leave the band as soon as the album was finished, but the rest of the members were hardly speaking to one another. To make matters worse, the tour lost $600,000 (equivalent to about $1.9 million in 2021).

CHAPTER 5:

LATER ALBUMS

TRIVIA TIME!

1. What was the working title of the album that was released as *The Final Cut*?

   a. *Another Brick*
   b. *Spare Bricks*
   c. *Over the Wall*
   d. *One Brick Short of a Load*

2. True or False: *The Final Cut* was the first and only Pink Floyd album that Rick Wright did not play on.

3. Which video game did Roger Waters and David Gilmour play during breaks in recording *The Final Cut* (before they had a falling out and began working separately)?

   a. Donkey Kong
   b. Pacman
   c. Centipede
   d. Frogger

4. Which composer, arranger, and instrumentalist replaced Rick Wright on keyboards for *The Final Cut* and also replaced Wright as the would-be mediator in disputes between Waters and Gilmour?

   a. Philip Glass

b. Rich Batsford

c. Andrew Lloyd Webber

d. Michael Kamen

5. True or False: *The Final Cut* reached No. 1 in both the UK and the US.

6. *The Final Cut* was the last Pink Floyd album for which band member?

a. David Gilmour

b. Nick Mason

c. Roger Waters

d. Rick Wright

7. True or False: Nick Mason had little involvement in *The Final Cut* except recording sound effects to be used on the album.

8. What was the name of the synthesizer-heavy band that included Rick Wright and released the album *Identity* in April 1984?

a. Free

b. Me

c. We

d. Zee

9. David Gilmour's houseboat *Astoria* included which of these features?

a. A tennis court

b. A recording studio

c. A tattoo parlor

d. A video-game arcade

10. The cover design for *A Momentary Lapse of Reason* was the

first Pink Floyd cover by Storm Thorgerson/Hipgnosis since which album?

   a. *The Dark Side of the Moon*
   b. *Wish You Were Here*
   c. *Animals*
   d. *The Wall*

11. True or False: After Roger Waters said the songs on *A Momentary Lapse of Reason* were "poor in general" and that David Gilmour's lyrics were "third-rate," Nick Mason said, "Roger's criticisms are fair."

12. Roger Waters's 1987 North American tour overlapped with Pink Floyd's. What was the name of Waters' tour?

   a. Radio K.A.O.S.
   b. Another Wall
   c. Still Waters
   d. Roger That

13. True or False: An agreement reached in 1987 allowed David Gilmour and Nick Mason to use the name "Pink Floyd" for future projects in perpetuity and gave Roger Waters exclusive rights to *The Wall*.

14. Rick Wright was credited as co-songwriter on five of the tracks on *The Division Bell*. These were his first songwriting credits since which previous album?

   a. *Animals*
   b. *Wish You Were Here*
   c. *The Dark Side of the Moon*
   d. *Meddle*

15. Who else helped David Gilmour write several tracks on *The Division Bell*?

a. The captain of Gilmour's boat *Astoria*
b. Gilmour's astrologer
c. Gilmour's future wife
d. Gilmour's attorney

16. True or False: Rick Wright's lead vocal on "Turning the Inside Out" from *The Division Bell* was his first lead vocal since "Time" on *The Dark Side of the Moon*.

17. Designer Storm Thorgerson said the Easter Island-like monoliths on the cover of *The Division Bell* were meant to represent what?

a. Sunrise and sunset
b. Good and evil
c. Words and music
d. The missing face of Syd Barrett

18. True or False: The final performance of The Division Bell Tour on October 29, 1994 was the last time Pink Floyd ever played live—except for a one-off reunion with Roger Waters in 2005.

19. Pink Floyd's last album to date, *The Endless River*, is entirely instrumental except for one track that includes lyrics. What is the title of that song?

a. "Calling"
b. "Louder Than Words"
c. "The Lost Art of Conversation"
d. "Unsung"

ANSWERS

1. b—*Spare Bricks*

2. True

3. a—Donkey Kong

4. d—Michael Kamen

5. False—*The Final Cut* reached No. 1 in the UK but peaked at No. 6 in the US.

6. c—Roger Waters

7. True

8. d—Zee

9. b—A recording studio. *A Momentary Lapse of Reason, On an Island* and the Division Bell were recorded there.

10. c—*Animals*

11. False—"Roger's criticisms are fair" was said by Rick Wright, not Nick Mason.

12. a—Radio K.A.O.S.

13. True

14. b—*Wish You Were Here*

15. c—Gilmour's future wife, Polly Samson.

16. True

17. d—Syd Barrett and Roger Waters

18. False. They also appeared in the Syd Barrett tribute concert

of 2007.

19. b — "Louder Than Words"

DID YOU KNOW?

- After *The Wall*, Roger Waters turned his attention to a project tentatively titled *Spare Bricks*, which he envisioned as the soundtrack for the film *Pink Floyd – The Wall*. But when the Falklands War between Britain and Argentina broke out in 1982, Waters switched gears and conceived an album dedicated to his father, who was killed in World War II.

- Waters planned to use some discarded songs from *The Wall* and new songs, while David Gilmour argued that the album should include only new material. When Gilmour asked for more time to write some new songs before recording started, Waters refused. In the end, Waters did lead vocals for all but one track and was credited with all the songwriting on the album that ended up being named *The Final Cut*.

- In 1986 Waters filed to dissolve Pink Floyd, calling the band "a spent force creatively." He asked EMI and Columbia to release him from any contractual obligations and then went to court to try and prevent the other members from using the name "Pink Floyd." Ultimately the legal and financial entanglements proved more complicated than first realized. All the parties reached an out-of-court settlement on Christmas Eve 1987 aboard Gilmour's houseboat *Astoria*, moored in the River Thames.

42

- In 1986, Gilmour began working with Nick Mason, Rick Wright, and other musicians on *A Momentary Lapse of Reason*. Legal complications prevented Wright from being reinstated as a full member of the band, so he was employed as a salaried player. Gilmour worked with several songwriters, eventually co-writing three songs with Anthony Moore.

- After a few years off, David Gilmour, Nick Mason, and Rick Wright assembled at Britannia Row Studios in January 1993 to begin work on a new album, *The Division Bell*. They improvised material for a couple weeks, then started writing songs from the most promising ideas. Bob Ezrin was hired as co-producer, and the project moved to Gilmour's boat for several months.

- David Gilmour and Nick Mason conceived *The Endless River* as a tribute to Rick Wright after his passing in 2008. The album included unused material recorded during sessions for *The Division Bell*, along with new tracks featuring various session musicians. *The Endless River* was released in November 2014. It reached No. 1 in the UK and No. 3 in the US. "I think we have successfully commandeered the best of what there is," said Gilmour. "It's a shame, but this is the end."

CHAPTER 6:

KEY PEOPLE

TRIVIA TIME!

1. Which of the following was <u>not</u> one of Roger Waters' roommates at Stanhope Gardens in London in the early 1960s?

   a. Nick Mason
   b. David Gilmour
   c. Bob Klose
   d. Syd Barrett

2. True or False: Roger Waters, Nick Mason, and Rick Wright first played together in a group founded by Syd Barrett.

3. Who did Syd Barrett replace as frontman of the band that eventually became Pink Floyd?

   a. Clive Metcalfe
   b. Sheilagh Noble
   c. Chris Dennis
   d. Bob Klose

4. Which of the following was <u>not</u> involved with promoting Pink Floyd in the band's early days?

   a. Brian Epstein
   b. Peter Jenner
   c. Andrew King

d. Bryan Morrison

5. Which hit single did David Gilmour say was the first record he ever bought?

    a. Chuck Berry's "Johnny B. Goode"
    b. Bill Haley's "Rock Around the Clock"
    c. Jerry Lee Lewis' "Great Balls of Fire"
    d. Buddy Holly's "Peggy Sue"

6. Which of the following guitarists has David Gilmour mentioned as an influence on his style?

    a. Jeff Beck
    b. Eric Clapton
    c. Jimi Hendrix
    d. All of the above

7. True or False: Pink Floyd paid tribute to Syd Barrett in the 1975 song suite "Shine On You Crazy Diamond" and on the 1979 album *The Wall*.

8. Who was the only person to play on every Pink Floyd album?

    a. Roger Waters
    b. Rick Wright
    c. Nick Mason
    d. David Gilmour

9. Which of the following Pink Floyd songs was <u>not</u> co-written by Nick Mason?

    a. "Echoes"
    b. "Careful with that Axe, Eugene"
    c. "One of These Days"
    d. "Money"

10. In addition to his music career, Nick Mason is also known for his deep involvement in which sport?

    a. Motor racing
    b. Tennis
    c. Cliff diving
    d. Cricket

11. Which of the following songs did <u>not</u> feature Rick Wright on lead vocals?

    a. "Us and Them"
    b. "Time"
    c. "Remember a Day"
    d. "Wearing the Inside Out"

12. True or False: Unlike Roger Waters, David Gilmour, and Nick Mason, Rick Wright made money from *The Wall* concert tour in 1980-81.

13. Which of these film scores was <u>not</u> written by Michael Kamen, who played keyboards in place of Rick Wright on *The Final Cut*?

    a. *Die Hard*
    b. *Mr. Holland's Opus*
    c. *Saving Private Ryan*
    d. *X-Men*

14. Which of the following Pink Floyd albums was <u>not</u> co-produced by Bob Ezrin?

    a. *The Wall*
    b. *Animals*
    c. *A Momentary Lapse of Reason*
    d. *The Division Bell*

15. When David Gilmour, Rick Wright, and Nick Mason performed at the funeral of Pink Floyd's longtime manager Steve O'Rourke in 2003, which former Pink Floyd session touring musician joined them?

   a. Jon Carin (keyboards)
   b. Guy Pratt (bass guitar)
   c. Dick Parry (saxophone)
   d. Clare Torry (vocalist)

16. Which of these songs was not part of Pink Floyd's set when they performed together for the first time in 24 years at the Live 8 concert in London in July 2005?

   a. "Speak to Me"/"Breathe"
   b. "Another Brick in the Wall (Part 2)"
   c. "Comfortably Numb"
   d. "Wish You Were Here"
   e. "Money"

17. True or False: In May 2007, the four living members of Pink Floyd performed together at a Syd Barrett tribute concert in London.

ANSWERS

1. b—David Gilmour

2. False—The group was founded by Keith Noble and Clive Metcalfe.

3. c—Chris Dennis

4. a—Brian Epstein

5. b—Bill Haley's "Rock Around the Clock"

6. d—All of the above

7. True

8. c—Nick Mason

9. d—"Money"

10. a—Motor racing

11. a—"Us and Them"

12. True—Because Wright was a salaried player and not a full member of the band, he did not share in the tour's loss of $600,000 (equivalent to about $1.9 million in 2021).

13. c—*Saving Private Ryan*

14. b—*Animals*

15. c—Dick Parry

16. b—"Another Brick in the Wall (Part 2)"

17. False—Gilmour, Wright, and Mason performed "Arnold Layne," and Waters performed "Flickering Flame" separately.

DID YOU KNOW?

- In addition to Pink Floyd's work, David Gilmour has released four solo albums and produced albums by many other artists. He is also an activist on issues including human rights, environmentalism, homelessness, poverty, and animal rights. In 2011, *Rolling Stone* magazine ranked him No. 14 among the greatest guitarists of all time, exclaiming, "His sprawling, elegant, relentlessly melodic solos were as bracing a wake-up call as those alarm clocks on *The Dark Side of the Moon.*"

- Steve O'Rourke became Pink Floyd's manager after Barrett's departure in 1968 and remained in that role until his death in 2003. Like Nick Mason and David Gilmour, O'Rourke was a passionate auto racer. In his Ferrari 512 BB, he finished 12th in the 24 Hours of Le Mans race in 1979. In 1991, he and Gilmour co-drove a Jaguar C-Type in the La Carrera Panamericana race in Mexico. O'Rourke suffered a broken leg in a crash during that race.

- Pink Floyd's *A Saucerful of Secrets* in 1968 was the first album cover created by Storm Thorgerson and his design group Hipgnosis. The company eventually developed some 250 album covers, including 12 for Pink Floyd as well as for solo albums by Syd Barrett, David Gilmour, and Nick Mason.

- Producer, arranger, and songwriter Bob Ezrin bridged the gap between the Pink Floyd dominated by Roger Waters and the Pink Floyd led by David Gilmour after Waters's departure. Ezrin was co-producer of *The Wall*, *A Momentary Lapse of Reason*, and *The Division Bell*. He has also worked with KISS, Alice Cooper, Peter Gabriel, Taylor Swift, Kansas, Lou Reed, Rod Stewart, and many other acts.

- Syd Barrett withdrew entirely from the music business in the late 1970s and moved in with his mother. Syd did not like to be reminded of his music career and was quite upset when fans sought him out. He reverted to his birth name, Roger Barrett, and lived a quiet life focused on gardening. However, he grew more comfortable with his legacy over time and even attended a signing for a book containing images from his rock star days.

CHAPTER 7:

SONGS OF THE EARLY YEARS

TRIVIA TIME!

1. Pink Floyd's first single, "Arnold Layne," was released in March 1967. What was the B-side of the single?

   a. "Candy and a Currant Bun"
   b. "Cotton Candy"
   c. "The Candy Man"
   d. "Big Rock Candy Mountain"

2. The title character of "Arnold Layne" has which strange habit?

   a. Picking his nose
   b. Chasing dogs while barking at them
   c. Taking women's underwear from clotheslines
   d. Sleeping in neighborhood sheds and garages

3. True or False: Pink Floyd's manager Andrew King said he paid radio stations to play "Arnold Layne."

4. Which song did Pink Floyd lip-synch to when they made their first UK national TV appearance on *Top of the Pops* in July 1967?

   a. "Arnold Layne"
   b. "See Emily Play"
   c. "Interstellar Overdrive"

d. "Matilda Mother"

5. Which song from *The Piper at the Gates of Dawn* was a completely instrumental improvisation created by all four of Pink Floyd's members?

   a. "Astronomy Domine"
   b. "Bike"
   c. "Lucifer Sam"
   d. "Interstellar Overdrive"

6. Which of Pink Floyd's early singles also appeared on a UK studio album at the same time?

   a. "Arnold Layne"
   b. "See Emily Run"
   c. "Flaming"
   d. "Point Me at the Sky"/"Careful with that Axe, Eugene"

7. Pink Floyd's business manager Peter Jenner said of the songs written by Syd Barrett for *A Saucerful of Secrets*, "I think every psychiatrist should be made to listen to those songs." Which of the songs mentioned by Jenner was ultimately included on the album?

   a. "Jugband Blues"
   b. "Scream Thy Last Scream"
   c. "The Vegetable Man"
   d. All of the above

8. Which track on *A Saucerful of Secrets* is believed to be the only recording in Pink Floyd history that features all five band members—Barrett, Gilmour, Mason, Waters, and Wright?

   a. "Corporal Clegg"

b. "Set the Controls for the Heart of the Sun"

c. "Let There Be More Light"

d. "Remember a Day"

9. In December 1968, Pink Floyd released a single with "Point Me at the Sky" on the A-side. Which song appeared on the B-side of the single and became much more popular with the fans than "Point Me at the Sky"?

   a. "Jugband Blues"

   b. "Scream Thy Last Scream"

   c. "Careful with that Axe, Eugene"

   d. "Set the Controls for the Heart of the Sun"

10. True or False: The single "Point Me at the Sky" is now one of the rarest of all Pink Floyd recordings.

11. "Careful with that Axe, Eugene" was also recorded and performed under different titles. Which of the following was not one of these titles?

   a. "The Crashing Waves"

   b. "Beset by Creatures of the Deep"

   c. "Come In Number 51, Your Time Is Up"

   d. "Explosion"

12. Which of the following songs was recorded in 1970 and often performed live, but not included on any Pink Floyd album except compilations many years later?

   a. "The Amazing Pudding"

   b. "Alan's Psychedelic Breakfast"

   c. "The Violent Sequence"

   d. "Embryo"

13. "One of These Days" from the album *Meddle* is completely

instrumental except for one line spoken by which member of Pink Floyd?

    a. David Gilmour
    b. Nick Mason
    c. Roger Waters
    d. Rick Wright

14. "One of These Days" includes a brief snippet from the theme song of which popular British TV show of that era?

    a. *The Avengers*
    b. *The Prisoner*
    c. *Doctor Who*
    d. *The Saint*

15. "Echoes" has been rumored to synchronize with the final 23 minutes of which film by Stanley Kubrick?

    a. *A Clockwork Orange*
    b. *2001: A Space Odyssey*
    c. *Dr. Strangelove*
    d. *Barry Lyndon*

16. True or False: Pink Floyd sued Andrew Lloyd Webber for allegedly plagiarizing the main riff from "Echoes" in the overture for *The Phantom of the Opera*.

17. "Us and Them" is quieter and more melodic than many earlier Pink Floyd songs, and it includes solos for which instrument near its beginning and end?

    a. Piano
    b. Organ
    c. Saxophone
    d. Harmonica

18. "Us and Them" includes a spoken-word part by which of these people?

    a. Roger Manifold (roadie)
    b. Alan Parsons (recording engineer)
    c. Chris Thomas (producer)
    d. Gerry O'Driscoll (studio doorman)

19. True or False: After Rick Wright shared lead vocals with David Gilmour on "Time," he did not have a lead-vocal credit again for more than 20 years.

ANSWERS

1. a—"Candy and a Currant Bun"

2. c—Taking women's underwear from clotheslines

3. True—King said, "We spent a couple hundred quid trying to buy it into the charts."

4. b—"See Emily Play"

5. d—"Interstellar Overdrive"

6. c—"Flaming"

7. a—"Jugband Blues"

8. b—"Set the Controls for the Heart of the Sun"

9. c—"Careful with that Axe, Eugene"

10. True

11. a—"The Crashing Waves"

12. d—"Embryo"

13. b—Nick Mason says, "One of these days, I'm going to cut you into little pieces."

14. c—Doctor Who

15. b—*2001: A Space Odyssey*

16. False—Waters said, "It's the same structure and it's the same notes and it's the same everything!"—but no lawsuit was ever filed.

17. c—Saxophone

18. a — Roger "The Hat" Manifold

19. True — Wright's next lead vocal was on *The Division Bell* album in 1994.

DID YOU KNOW?

- Pink Floyd did not tend to shoot for success with individual songs such as the catchy two- or two-and-a-half-minute singles that typically dominated the Top 40. The band focused mainly on albums, each of which was supposed to affect the listener in a way that transcended the sum of its parts.

- In January 1967, Pink Floyd recorded five songs, all written by Syd Barrett, at Sound Techniques Studio in Chelsea. Among them was "Arnold Layne," which was released as the band's first single in March. "We knew we wanted to be rock 'n' roll stars and we wanted to make singles," Nick Mason said, "so it seemed like the most suitable song to condense into three minutes without losing too much."

- The songs that Syd Barrett wrote for *A Saucerful of Secrets* ("Jugband Blues," "Scream Thy Last Scream," and "The Vegetable Man") have often been interpreted as reflecting his descent into schizophrenia.

- "Echoes," written by all four members of Pink Floyd, runs for over 23 minutes and occupies the entire second side of *Meddle* in vinyl and cassette versions. Assembled from a variety of separate fragments, the track includes extended instrumental portions, ambient sound effects, and various improvisations. Rick Wright composed the lengthy piano intro and the main chord progressions, and Roger Waters wrote all the lyrics.

Waters said "Echoes" was the genesis of the themes further explored on *The Dark Side of the Moon*.

- The tracks on *The Dark Side of the Moon* were performed live many times and further refined before recording began on the album. The album relied heavily on tools such as multitrack recording, tape loops, ambient sounds, and the analog synthesizer, while omitting the extended instrumentals that were typical of earlier projects.

CHAPTER 8:

SONGS OF LATER YEARS

TRIVIA TIME!

1. In the album version of "Wish You Were Here," the song segues from "Have a Cigar" with which of these sound effects?

    a. Church bells chiming
    b. An AM radio tuning through several stations
    c. Dogs barking
    d. A brief excerpt from "God Save the Queen"

2. When Pink Floyd was inducted into the Rock & Roll Hall of Fame in 1996, David Gilmour and Rick Wright played "Wish You Were Here" with which musician?

    a. Eric Clapton
    b. George Harrison
    c. Billy Corgan
    d. The Edge

3. What did David Gilmour do later on the same day that Syd Barrett visited the recording studio?

    a. Drove in an auto race
    b. Went scuba diving
    c. Got married
    d. Completed the final test for his pilot's license

4. True or False: Like "Atom Heart Mother" and "Echoes"

from previous albums, "Shine On You Crazy Diamond" takes up one whole side of the *Wish You Were Here* album.

5. What was the original title of the song "Sheep" on the *Animals* album?

   a. "Raving and Drooling"
   b. "Fussing and Fighting"
   c. "Moving and Shaking"
   d. "Coming and Going"

6. Which song from *The Wall* became Pink Floyd's first No. 1 single in the United States?

   a. "Comfortably Numb"
   b. "Run Like Hell"
   c. "Don't Leave Me Now"
   d. "Another Brick in the Wall (Part 2)"

7. "Another Brick in the Wall (Part 2)" was intended as a protest against what?

   a. Wearing of furs
   b. Rigid and arbitrary discipline in schools
   c. Nuclear power
   d. Discrimination against LGBTQ people

8. True or False: At the suggestion of producer Bob Ezrin, David Gilmour grudgingly agreed to add a brief disco riff to "Another Brick in the Wall (Part 2)."

9. Which of the following songs includes "the greatest guitar solo of all time," according to a listener poll by the digital radio station Planet Rock?

   a. "Another Brick in the Wall (Part 2)"

b. "Run Like Hell"

c. "Comfortably Numb"

d. "Hey You"

10. Which member of Pink Floyd said, "I think things like 'Comfortably Numb' were the last embers of mine and Roger's ability to work collaboratively together"?

a. David Gilmour

b. Nick Mason

c. Rick Wright

d. None of the above

11. Which song was the only one on *The Final Cut* album featuring lead vocals by David Gilmour?

a. "The Postwar Dream"

b. "Not Now John"

c. "The Hero Returns"

d. "The Final Cut"

12. True or False: In the song "Not Now John" from *The Final Cut*, "John" refers to British politician John Major.

13. Which of the following people did <u>not</u> serve as co-writer with David Gilmour on the song "Learning to Fly" from *A Momentary Lapse of Reason*?

a. Jon Carin

b. Bob Ezrin

c. Rick Wright

d. Anthony Moore

14. Which of the following songs from *A Momentary Lapse of Reason* was <u>not</u> released as a single?

a. "Learning to Fly"

b. "The Dogs of War"

c. "On the Turning Away"

d. "One Slip"

15. From which classic novel are the opening lines of the song "Sorrow" taken?

    a. William Faulkner's *The Sound and the Fury*

    b. Ernest Hemingway's *A Farewell to Arms*

    c. John Steinbeck's *The Grapes of Wrath*

    d. Vladimir Nabokov's *Lolita*

16. The song "Keep Talking" from *The Division Bell* includes a brief sample of which famous scientist's voice?

    a. Stephen Hawking

    b. Carl Sagan

    c. Jonas Salk

    d. Neil deGrasse Tyson

17. True or False: The song "High Hopes" from *The Division Bell* was co-written by David Gilmour, Nick Mason, and Rick Wright.

ANSWERS

1. b — An AM radio tuning through several stations

2. c — Billy Corgan

3. c — Got married to his first wife, Ginger Hasenbein

4. False — The song is divided into different parts that open and close the album.

5. a — "Raving and Drooling"

6. d — "Another Brick in the Wall (Part 2)"

7. b — Rigid and arbitrary discipline in schools

8. True

9. c — "Comfortably Numb"

10. a — David Gilmour

11. b — "Not Now John"

12. False — Although several public figures are mentioned by name in the song, "John" is used as one would use "buddy" or some other generic term for someone whose name is unknown to the speaker.

13. c — Rick Wright

14. b — "The Dogs of War"

15. c — John Steinbeck's *The Grapes of Wrath*

16. a — Stephen Hawking

17. False — The song was written by Gilmour and his second wife, Polly Samson.

DID YOU KNOW?

- "Another Brick in the Wall" was a three-part song suite that appeared on *The Wall* album. Its second part became Pink Floyd's first No. 1 single in the United States, and it also reached No. 1 in the UK, Austria, Canada, Finland, France, Germany, Ireland, Israel, New Zealand, Norway, Portugal, South Africa, Sweden, and Switzerland.

- "Run Like Hell" is written from the point of view of *The Wall*'s main character, an embittered and alienated rock star named Pink, whose concert audience turns into an angry mob during his drug-induced hallucination. It is the only song on *The Wall* album to feature a keyboard solo by Rick Wright, but Wright had solos on other songs during live performances.

- "On the Turning Away" from *A Momentary Lapse of Reason* is unusual for Pink Floyd songs in the post-Waters era because it is an overtly political protest song. (During work on *The Final Cut,* Gilmour had become fed up with Waters's politicizing.) Often described as a power ballad, it is one of Pink Floyd's most musically complex songs. Guitarist Guy Pratt, who played on the tour that supported the album, said, "The song only has five chords on it, but they don't necessarily show up where you think they will."

- The song "High Hopes" from *The Division Bell* refers to things that people gain and lose over the course of their lives. David Gilmour maintained that the theme of loss in the song relates to his own personal life — leaving his hometown and his childhood behind — and not necessarily to the band's loss of Syd Barrett and then Roger Waters.

- Rivers have important symbolic meaning in Pink Floyd lore. The final couplet of "High Hopes" ("The endless river/Forever and ever") echoes a line from the 1967 song "See Emily Play" ("Float on a river/Forever and ever"). It also previews the title of Pink Floyd's final studio album, *The Endless River*, released in 2014. The cover art portrays a young man sailing his boat through a river. Some have speculated that the figure represents departed member Richard Wright sailing towards eternity.

CHAPTER 9:

LIVE PERFORMANCES AND TOURS

TRIVIA TIME!

1. True or False: The band that eventually became known as Pink Floyd played mostly covers of R&B hits during their earliest live performances in 1965 and 1966.

2. Which famous musician attended Pink Floyd's performance at the launch of the underground newspaper *International Times* at the famous Roundhouse Club in October 1966?

   a. Cliff Richard
   b. Paul McCartney
   c. John Lennon
   d. Keith Richards

3. Which of these acts did <u>not</u> share the bill with Pink Floyd at the first free Hyde Park concert in London in June 1968?

   a. Roy Harper
   b. T. Rex
   c. Black Sabbath
   d. Jethro Tull

4. Which of the following things did <u>not</u> happen on stage during Pink Floyd's show called "The Final Lunacy" at Royal Albert Hall in June 1969?

a. A cannon was fired
b. A crew member dressed as a gorilla cavorted
c. A ballerina performed
d. Rick Wright sawed wood

5. Which of these early Pink Floyd albums did not have a concert tour named after it?

   a. *Ummagumma*
   b. *Atom Heart Mother*
   c. *Meddle*
   d. *The Dark Side of the Moon*

6. True or False: The largest crowd to ever see a Pink Floyd performance showed up at an outdoor concert in Paris in September 1970.

7. Which element introduced in 1974 became a staple of Pink Floyd's live shows for years thereafter?

   a. A half-scale replica of Stonehenge
   b. A high-definition, circular projection panel called "Mr. Screen"
   c. An inflatable equestrian statue of Queen Elizabeth II
   d. A giant reproduction of Andy Warhol's *Portrait of Mao Zedong*

8. Which seminal work of Pink Floyd's did David Gilmour credit for the transition from small venues where "you could hear a pin drop" to giant stadiums?

   a. The album *The Dark Side of the Moon*
   b. The song "Us and Them"
   c. The song "Time"
   d. The song "Money"

9. Which giant inflatable animal floated over audiences

during the In the Flesh Tour in 1977?

a. A pig named Algie
b. A dog named Rufus
c. A sheep named Dolly
d. A cow named Elsie

10. True or False: The In the Flesh Tour, following the release of the *Animals* album, proved a disappointment in terms of attendance and revenue.

11. Which member of Pink Floyd expressed his dislike for giant venues and his annoyance with rowdy fans during the In the Flesh Tour?

a. David Gilmour
b. Nick Mason
c. Roger Waters
d. Rick Wright

12. True or False: The Wall Tour of 1980-81 was Pink Floyd's most extensive and lucrative to date.

13. Which of these was not one of the characters represented by inflatable figures designed by Gerald Scarfe for The Wall Tour?

a. "The Schoolmaster"
b. "The Sea Captain"
c. "The Mother"
d. "The Ex-Wife"

14. True or False: The A Momentary Lapse of Reason Tour was the most lucrative tour in the world for 1987 and 1988.

15. The stage sets for which Pink Floyd concert tour were not designed by British architect Mark Fisher?

a. In the Flesh Tour
b. The Wall Tour
c. A Momentary Lapse of Reason Tour
d. The Division Bell Tour

16. Who did <u>not</u> perform with the others at business manager Steve O'Rourke's funeral in 2003?

a. Roger Waters
b. Rick Wright
c. Nick Mason
d. David Gilmour

17. Which of these Pink Floyd songs was the last ever performed in public by four of the living members together in 2005?

a. "Another Brick in the Wall (Part 2)"
b. "Comfortably Numb"
c. "Money"
d. "Wish You Were Here"

18. Which of the following is not one of Pink Floyd's live albums?

a. *Delicate Sound of Thunder*
b. *Pulse*
c. *Is Anybody Out There?*
d. *A Collection of Great Dance Songs*

ANSWERS

1. True

2. b — Paul McCartney

3. c — Black Sabbath

4. c — A ballerina performed

5. a — *Ummagumma* (Pink Floyd's 1969 tour was called The Man and the Journey Tour.)

6. True — The crowd was estimated at 500,000.

7. b — A high-definition, circular projection panel called "Mr. Screen"

8. d — The song "Money" (Gilmour said that crowds would yell, "Play 'Money'! Gimme something I can shake my ass to!")

9. a — A pig named Algie

10. False — Although *Animals* had not sold as well as *The Dark Side of the Moon* or *Wish You Were Here*, the tour set new attendance records at venues all around the world.

11. c — Roger Waters

12. False — The tour was Pink Floyd's most elaborate in terms of staging, but it only visited four locations — Los Angeles, California; Uniondale, New York; Dortmund, Germany; and London — and ended up losing money.

13. b — "The Sea Captain"

14. True

15. c — A Momentary Lapse of Reason Tour

16. a — Roger Waters

17. b — "Comfortably Numb"

18. d — *A Collection of Great Dance Songs*

DID YOU KNOW?

- From their earliest days, Pink Floyd made high sound quality and innovative visual effects key elements of their live performances. Their "psychedelic" music and slide-and-light shows during small club gigs in London helped the band differentiate itself from others and attract their first batch of loyal followers. Their early road manager Peter Wynne-Wilson used polarizers, mirrors, and even stretched condoms to alter the typical lighting effects.

- Pink Floyd performed at many events in and around London in their early days, separately from their concert tours. One of these was the first free Hyde Park concert on June 29, 1968, which was sort of a precursor to the giant music festivals that soon followed. "The one in '68 was wonderful," Nick Mason said, "because it was much more a picnic in the park than a mini-Woodstock. A lovely day." Pink Floyd appeared at the Hyde Park free concert again in 1970.

- During The Wall Tour in 1980-81, "Comfortably Numb" was performed with Waters, dressed as a doctor, at the bottom of the wall, and Gilmour on top of the wall with spotlights behind him. "Roger's just finishing singing his thing, and I'm standing there waiting," Gilmour said. "I'm in pitch darkness and no one knows I'm there yet. And suddenly there's all this light up there and the sound's coming out and everything. Every night there's this sort of gasp from about 15,000 people. And that's quite something, let me tell you."

- Pink Floyd's first post-Waters album, *A Momentary Lapse of Reason*, was supported by an 11-week "promotional" tour in late 1987 that eventually extended into two tours for almost two years and included about 200 concerts attended by some 5.5 million people. The tour included Pink Floyd's first performances ever in Russia, Norway, Spain, and New Zealand. The first leg of the tour was documented on the *Delicate Sound of Thunder* album and video.

- The Division Bell Tour in 1994 featured perhaps more elaborate sets and special effects than any of its predecessors — including two custom-designed working airships and a 130-foot-tall arch modeled after the Hollywood Bowl. The tour was documented on the *Pulse* album and video.

CHAPTER 10:

MOVIES, TELEVISION, AND VIDEOS

TRIVIA TIME!

1. True or False: Pink Floyd regularly made music videos from the very beginning of their recording career.

2. Which member of Pink Floyd was annoyed at appearing on TV to promote "See Emily Play" in 1967 and said, "John Lennon doesn't have to do *Top of the Pops*"?

   a. Syd Barrett
   b. Nick Mason
   c. Roger Waters
   d. Rick Wright

3. Which of the following celebrities did not appear in the documentary *Tonite Let's All Make Love in London*, the first film to feature Pink Floyd?

   a. Julie Christie
   b. Lee Marvin
   c. Albert Finney
   d. Michael Caine

4. True or False: Pink Floyd's identification with "space rock" led to their being invited to perform on a live BBC telecast celebrating the Apollo 11 moon landing in July 1969.

5. Which of the following films from the late 1960s and early

1970s does <u>not</u> have a soundtrack by Pink Floyd?

   a. *The Committee*
   b. *More*
   c. *La Vallee*
   d. *Two-Lane Blacktop*

6. The documentary originally titled *Syd Barrett: Crazy Diamond* shows Barrett's final London concert on June 6, 1970. Who was onstage with Barrett when he abruptly walked off the stage after only four numbers?

   a. Rick Wright
   b. Nick Mason
   c. David Gilmour
   d. Roger Waters

7. What is the title of the first full-length concert documentary film featuring Pink Floyd, released in 1972?

   a. *Pink Floyd: Live in London*
   b. *Pink Floyd: Live at Pompeii*
   c. *Pink Floyd: Live at Budokan*
   d. *Pink Floyd: Live at Madison Square Garden*

8. Which 1975 film did the members of Pink Floyd, and other rock bands, help to finance?

   a. *Monty Python and the Holy Grail*
   b. *The Rocky Horror Picture Show*
   c. *Royal Flash*
   d. *Lisztomania*

9. True or False: Bob Geldof was the only singer/actor considered for the role of Pink in the feature film *Pink Floyd – The Wall*.

10. Which of the following is <u>not</u> a film by Alan Parker, the director of *Pink Floyd — The Wall*?

   a. *Angel Heart*
   b. *Mississippi Burning*
   c. *Driving Miss Daisy*
   d. *The Commitments*

11. In *Pink Floyd — The Wall*, the character Pink is writing a poem in school when the teacher snatches the paper from him and sarcastically reads it aloud. Which song is the poem taken from?

   a. "Money"
   b. "Point Me to the Sky"
   c. "Brain Damage"
   d. "Welcome to the Machine"

12. Which of the following statements is <u>not</u> true of the film *Pink Floyd — The Wall*?

   a. Plans for the movie were afoot even before *The Wall* album was released
   b. Director Alan Parker said it was one of the best experiences of his career
   c. It received "two thumbs up" from film critics Roger Ebert and Gene Siskel
   d. It won British Academy of Film and Television Award (BAFTA) awards for Best Original Song and Best Sound.

13. Which Pink Floyd member said, "The movie was the less successful telling of *The Wall* story as opposed to the album and concert versions" in the BBC/VH1 documentary *Behind the Wall*?

   a. David Gilmour

b. Nick Mason

c. Roger Waters

d. Rick Wright

14. When Willie Christie directed the film *The Final Cut*, released in 1983, what was his relationship to Roger Waters?

    a. His barber

    b. His tax accountant

    c. His next-door neighbor

    d. His brother-in-law

15. True or False: Storm Thorgerson, who was known for designing many Pink Floyd album covers, also directed several of the band's music videos.

16. Which of these people did <u>not</u> direct any Pink Floyd music videos?

    a. Gerald Scarfe

    b. Willie Christie

    c. Aubrey Powell

    d. John Landis

17. True or False: The film *La Carrera Panamericana* (1992) shows footage of concerts in Latin America during Pink Floyd's A Momentary Lapse of Reason Tour.

18. Which of the following films is <u>not</u> a concert documentary?

    a. *Pink Floyd: Live at Pompeii*

    b. *Delicate Sound of Thunder*

    c. *The Final Cut*

    d. *Pulse*

19. Which of these is an actual film produced for the BBC Two's

Omnibus series, broadcast in 2001 and released on DVD in 2003?

a. *The Pink Floyd and Syd Barrett Story*
b. *Deep Waters*
c. *David Gilmour: Guitar Master*
d. *The Wright Stuff*

20. The behind-the-scenes documentary *The Story of Wish You Were Here*, released in 2012, includes footage of which two Pink Floyd members performing excerpts from the original songs?

a. Rick Wright and Roger Waters
b. Roger Waters and David Gilmour
c. David Gilmour and Nick Mason
d. Nick Mason and Rick Wright

ANSWERS

1. True—Pink Floyd made a video of their first single, "Arnold Layne."

2. a—Syd Barrett

3. c—Albert Finney

4. True—Pink Floyd played an improvised instrumental piece called "Moonhead."

5. d—*Two-Lane Blacktop*

6. c—David Gilmour

7. b—*Pink Floyd: Live at Pompeii*

8. a—*Monty Python and the Holy Grail*

9. False—Roger Waters was considered for the role before Geldof was hired.

10. c—*Driving Miss Daisy*

11. a—"Money"

12. b—Parker actually called the project "one of the most miserable experiences of my creative life."

13. a—David Gilmour

14. d—His brother-in-law

15. True—Thorgerson directed the videos for "Learning to Fly," "The Dogs of War," and "High Hopes."

16. d—John Landis

17. False — The film documents an auto race in Mexico in which David Gilmour, Nick Mason, and manager Steve O'Rourke competed.

18. c — *The Final Cut* tells a fictional story seen through the eyes of a World War II veteran (played by Alex McAvoy, who also played the Teacher in *Pink Floyd – The Wall*).

19. a — *The Pink Floyd and Syd Barrett Story*

20. b — Roger Waters and David Gilmour

DID YOU KNOW?

- Pink Floyd was featured in Tonite Let's All Make Love in London, a documentary film by Peter Whitehead about the "swinging London scene" of the late 1960s. Shot in 1967 and released in 1968, the film includes a performance of "Interstellar Overdrive," along with footage and interviews of celebrities who attended. An expanded soundtrack album called Pink Floyd & Friends — Interstellar Overdrive was released in 2001.

- Pink Floyd also contributed three songs to Michelangelo Antonioni's Zabriskie Point (1970). A track written by Rick Wright and then called "The Violent Sequence," which Antonioni rejected, later became "Us and Them." Zabriskie Point featured a title song written and recorded by Roy Orbison, as well as songs by the Rolling Stones, the Grateful Dead, and the Youngbloods.

- Taken together, The Wall album and the feature film based upon it are one of the most ambitious projects ever attempted by a popular musician — in this case, Roger Waters. The film was originally supposed to be built around actual concert footage, with animations by Gerald Scarfe and a few dramatic scenes mixed in, but those plans were changed when Bob Geldof (not Waters) was given the role of Pink.

- During production of Pink Floyd — The Wall, tensions ran high among Waters, director Alan Parker, and production designer/animator Gerald Scarfe. Waters called the filming "a very unnerving and unpleasant experience." Despite the difficulties, the film was generally well received. The world premiere in July 1982 was attended by many celebrities, including Pete Townshend, Sting, Steven Spielberg, and Roger Taylor. Pink Floyd — The Wall earned BAFTA awards for Best Original Song ("Another Brick in the Wall") and Best Sound. Film critic Roger Ebert added it to his "Great Movies" list in 2010.

- The Pink Floyd and Syd Barrett Story focuses on the band's first lead songwriter, guitarist, and singer. The film has also been presented as Syd Barrett: Crazy Diamond and Pink Floyd & Syd Barrett. It includes interviews with Gilmour, Mason, Waters, Wright, and their former bandmate Bob Klose, along with concert footage. Barrett's sister said that he watched the film when it was aired on the BBC in 2001 and found it to be "too loud."

CHAPTER 11:

SOLO AND SIDE PROJECTS

TRIVIA TIME!

1. True or False: Both Roger Waters and David Gilmour are listed as producers of Syd Barrett's first solo album, *The Madcap Laughs*.

2. Which of these musicians did <u>not</u> play on and help to produce Syd Barrett's second solo album, *Barrett*?

   a. David Gilmour
   b. Jerry Shirley
   c. Roger Waters
   d. Rick Wright

3. Which of the following musicians called Syd Barrett's album *The Madcap Laughs* one of his favorite albums of all time?

   a. Bryan Ferry
   b. David Bowie
   c. Bono
   d. George Harrison

4. Which of the following was the first solo album released by a Pink Floyd member while the four post-Barrett bandmates were still together?

   a. *David Gilmour*

b. *Wet Dream* by Rick Wright

c. *Nick Mason's Fictitious Sports*

d. *The Pros and Cons of Hitch Hiking* by Roger Waters

5. True or False: Pete Townshend supplied lyrics for a tune written by David Gilmour that appeared on Gilmour's *About Face* album.

6. Which singer has David Gilmour worked with extensively since helping her to get her first recording contract?

   a. Madonna
   b. Cyndi Lauper
   c. Kate Bush
   d. Adele

7. Which musician has <u>not</u> worked on Nick Mason's solo and side projects?

   a. Robert Wyatt
   b. Adrian Belew
   c. Rick Fenn
   d. Michael Mantler

8. True or False: Rick Wright called the album *Identity*, released by his band Zee in 1984, "an experiment best forgotten."

9. Which David Gilmour solo album did Rick Wright <u>not</u> play on?

   a. *About Face*
   b. *On an Island*
   c. *Live in Gdansk*
   d. *Rattle that Lock*

10. Which former member of Pink Floyd (from the band's early days) played guitar on Gilmour's albums *On an Island* and

Rattle that Lock?

a. Chris Dennis
b. Keith Noble
c. Bob Klose
d. Clive Metcalfe

11. Which of these singers contributed lead vocals on two tracks from Rick Wright's solo album *Broken China*?

a. Jewel
b. Sinead O'Connor
c. Kate Bush
d. Sade

12. True or False: David Gilmour, Nick Mason, Roger Waters, and Rick Wright each released at least one solo album while still a member of Pink Floyd.

13. Which artist played lead guitar on most of the tracks for Roger Waters's first solo album, *The Pros and Cons of Hitch Hiking*?

a. Eric Clapton
b. Jeff Beck
c. The Edge
d. David Gilmour

14. Which of the following is <u>not</u> one of Roger Waters's solo albums?

a. *Radio K.A.O.S.*
b. *Amused to Death*
c. *Still Waters*
d. *Is This the Life We Really Want?*

15. Which artist performed lead vocals on "Comfortably

Numb" backed by The Band at *The Wall – Live in Berlin* concert in 1990?

a. Paul Young
b. David Bowie
c. Bono
d. Van Morrison

16. True or False: One of Roger Waters's solo projects is *Ca Ira*, an opera set during the French Revolution.

17. For his second and last solo album, *Broken China* (1996), Rick Wright used members of which musician's touring band?

a. Peter Gabriel
b. David Bowie
c. Van Morrison
d. Bruce Springsteen

18. Which of Roger Waters's solo albums was not supported by a world tour?

a. *The Pros and Cons of Hitch Hiking*
b. *Radio K.A.O.S.*
c. *Amused to Death*
d. *Is This the Life We Really Want?*

19. True or False: David Gilmour, Nick Mason, and Roger Waters performed together once during Waters's The Wall Live Tour.

20. What is the name of the band that Nick Mason formed in 2018 to perform vintage Pink Floyd songs?

a. Stonemason
b. Nick Mason's Saucerful of Secrets
c. The Gates of Dawn

d. Nick and the Knives

ANSWERS

1. True—The album was recorded off and on for many months, with five different producers each running separate recording sessions.

2. c—Roger Waters

3. b—David Bowie

4. a—*David Gilmour*

5. False—Townshend provided the lyrics as requested, but Gilmour decided not to use them. The song ended up as "White City Fighting" (featuring guitar work by Gilmour) on Townshend's album *White City: A Novel*.

6. c—Kate Bush

7. b—Adrian Belew

8. True

9. a—*About Face*

10. c—Bob Klose. He had last played with the band in 1965, before Gilmour joined.

11. b—Sinead O'Connor

12. False—Waters did not work with Pink Floyd again after his first solo album was released in 1984.

13. a—Eric Clapton

14. c—*Still Waters*

15. d—Van Morrison

16. True—The opera was released as a double CD and reached No. 5 on the US Classical Music charts in 2005.

17. a—Peter Gabriel

18. c—Although *Amused to Death* (1992) is Waters's most successful solo album to date, the material was not performed live until the In the Flesh Tour in 1999.

19. True—They performed "Comfortably Numb" and "Outside the Wall" together at the O2 Arena in London on May 12, 2011.

20. b—Nick Mason's Saucerful of Secrets

DID YOU KNOW?

- Although Syd Barrett has become legendary as the original leader of Pink Floyd and the main songwriter, singer, guitarist, and visionary of the band's early days, his career was remarkably short. After he was ousted from the band in 1968, he released one single ("Octopus") in 1969 and two albums (The Madcap Laughs and Barrett) in 1970 before retiring from the music business. Both albums are highly critically acclaimed.

- In the late 1970s, David Gilmour came to believe that his talents were being underused in Pink Floyd, which was then dominated by Roger Waters. "Roger was in full flow with the ideas," Nick Mason said, "but he was really keeping Dave down and frustrating him deliberately." Gilmour released his first solo album, David Gilmour, in 1978. Seeing The Final Cut as virtually a Waters solo album, Gilmour went to work on his second solo album, About Face.

- Rick Wright's first solo album, Wet Dream, was released in September 1978. After years of being in and out of favor with his bandmates, Wright was reinvigorated by his successful contributions to The Division Bell, and he came out with his second solo album, Broken China, in 1996. He played regularly on Gilmour's recordings and tours for the rest of his life.

- To date, Roger Waters has released five studio albums, four live albums (each also a video album), one compilation, one box set, and an opera. In July 1990, soon after the fall of the Berlin Wall, Waters staged The Wall—Live in Berlin. One of the largest concerts in history, the event drew an estimated 200,000 spectators and featured Van Morrison, The Band, Joni Mitchell, Cyndi Lauper, Bryan Adams, The Hooters, Scorpions, Paul Carrack, Marianne Faithfull, Thomas Dolby, and Sinead O'Connor.

- Roger Waters toured extensively from 1999 through 2013. When he kicked off his The Wall Live Tour in 2010, he said, "I have a swan song in me, and I think this will probably be it." By the time the tour concluded in 2013, it was the highest-grossing tour of all time by a solo artist. The record has since been broken by Ed Sheeran.

CHAPTER 12:

HONORS AND AWARDS

TRIVIA TIME!

1. Which Pink Floyd song won the BAFTA for Best Original Song in 1983?

    a. "Goodbye Blue Sky"
    b. "Another Brick in the Wall"
    c. "Goodbye Cruel World"
    d. "Is Anybody Out There?"

2. True or False: No Pink Floyd single has ever won a Grammy award.

3. Which of the following artists did not attend Pink Floyd's induction into the Rock & Roll Hall of Fame in 1996?

    a. David Gilmour
    b. Nick Mason
    c. Roger Waters
    d. Rick Wright

4. True or False: Syd Barrett was not mentioned when Pink Floyd was inducted into the Rock & Roll Hall of Fame.

5. Which artist inducted Pink Floyd into the Rock & Roll Hall of Fame?

    a. Eric Clapton
    b. Paul McCartney

c. Bono

d. Billy Corgan

6. Which artist was <u>not</u> enshrined in the Rock & Roll Hall of Fame during the same ceremony as Pink Floyd in 1996?

a. Steve Winwood

b. David Bowie

c. Jefferson Airplane

d. The Velvet Underground

7. Which song was performed during Pink Floyd's induction ceremony at the Rock & Roll Hall of Fame?

a. "Comfortably Numb"

b. "Wish You Were Here"

c. "Another Brick in the Wall (Part 2)"

d. "Money"

8. Where did Colin Larkin, founder and editor of the *Encyclopedia of Popular Music*, rank Pink Floyd in his "Top 50 Artists of All Time"?

a. Between No. 1 and No. 12

b. Between No. 13 and No. 25

c. Between No. 26 and No. 37

d. Between No. 38 and No. 50

9. Not including movie soundtracks, Pink Floyd released twelve studio albumswhen Colin Larkin published his "All-Time Top 1000 Album List" in 2000. How many of them were not included in the list?

a. One

b. Two

c. Three

d. Four

10. Which member of Pink Floyd was made a Commander of the Order of the British Empire (CBE) by Queen Elizabeth II in June 2003?

    a. Rick Wright
    b. Roger Waters
    c. Nick Mason
    d. David Gilmour

11. Which magazine named Pink Floyd the "biggest band of all time" in 2011?

    a. *Guitar Player*
    b. *Rolling Stone*
    c. *Q*
    d. *New Musical Express*

12. True or False: Pink Floyd was enshrined in the UK Music Hall of Fame in 2004, the first year of the organization's existence.

13. Which artist inducted Pink Floyd into the UK Music Hall of Fame?

    a. Sting
    b. Jimmy Page
    c. Pete Townshend
    d. Rod Stewart

14. Who did David Gilmour induct into the UK Music Hall of Fame in 2006?

    a. Queen
    b. Led Zeppelin
    c. Jimi Hendrix
    d. Brian Wilson

15. True or False: Two Pink Floyd albums, *The Dark Side of the Moon* and *The Wall*, have been selected for the Grammy Hall of Fame.

16. Which British artist did <u>not</u> receive the Polar Music Prize before Pink Floyd was honored in 2008?

    a. Paul McCartney
    b. Peter Gabriel
    c. Elton John
    d. Led Zeppelin

17. Which of the following was <u>not</u> a *Q* magazine award won by Pink Floyd?

    a. Best Live Act of 1994: Pink Floyd
    b. No. 1 of the 100 Greatest Songs Ever, 2006: "Comfortably Numb"
    c. Outstanding Contribution to Music, 2008: David Gilmour
    d. Classic Albums of All Time, 2014: *The Dark Side of the Moon*

18. Where did *Rolling Stone* rank Pink Floyd among its 100 Greatest Artists of All Time in 2011?

    a. Between No. 1 and No. 25
    b. Between No. 26 and No. 50
    c. Between No. 51 and No. 75
    d. Between No. 76 and No. 100

19. Which British band was the only one to appear on a UK postage stamp prior to Pink Floyd in 2016?

    a. The Beatles
    b. The Rolling Stones

c. Queen

d. The Who

20. Which member of Pink Floyd was made a Commander of the Order of the British Empire (CBE) by Prince William, Duke of Cambridge, in May 2019?

a. Rick Wright

b. Roger Waters

c. Nick Mason

d. David Gilmour

ANSWERS

1. b — "Another Brick in the Wall"

2. True — "Marooned" from *The Division Bell* won for best rock instrumental performance in 1995.

3. c — Roger Waters

4. False — Barrett did not attend the ceremony, but he was enshrined with his former bandmates.

5. d — Billy Corgan

6. a — Steve Winwood

7. b — "Wish You Were Here"

8. a — Pink Floyd was ranked No. 3.

9. c — Two (*Ummagumma, The Final Cut*)

10. d — David Gilmour

11. c — *Q Magazine*

12. False — Pink Floyd was inducted in the UK Hall of Fame's second year, 2005.

13. c — Pete Townshend

14. d — Brian Wilson

15. True — *The Dark Side of the Moon* was selected in 1999 and *The Wall* in 2008.

16. B — Peter Gabriel received the award in 2009, one year after Pink Floyd.

17. b — "Comfortably Numb" ("Live Forever" by Oasis won the award.)

18. c — Pink Floyd was ranked No. 51.

19. a — The Beatles

20. c — Nick Mason

DID YOU KNOW?

- During Pink Floyd's heyday, the Grammy Awards for popular music tended to focus mainly on Top 40 hits. Pink Floyd won a competitive Grammy only twice. Recording engineer James Guthrie won for best engineered non-classical album for The Wall in 1981, and the band won for best rock instrumental performance for "Marooned" in 1995. The albums The Dark Side of the Moon and The Wall have been honored in the Grammy Hall of Fame.

- Pink Floyd's citation for the Rock & Roll Hall of Fame reads as follows: "Pink Floyd were the architects of two major music movements—psychedelic space-rock and blues-based progressive rock—and became known for their biting political, social and emotional commentary. With 1973's Dark Side of The Moon and 1979's The Wall, the band created two of the most ambitious (and best-selling) albums of all time—and underscored that personal torment could resonate on a massive level."

- Colin Larkin, founder and editor of the Encyclopedia of Popular Music, ranked Pink Floyd No. 3 on his list "The 50 Greatest Artists of All Time." He also developed the "All-Time Album Top 1000 List," first published in 1994 and updated in 1998 and 2000. The 2000 version, which reflected a synthesis of critics' polls and votes from some 200,000 music fans, included ten albums by Pink Floyd as well as Syd Barrett's solo album The Madcap Laughs.

- Pink Floyd albums on the 2000 Larkin list were The Dark Side of the Moon (No. 9), The Wall (30), Wish You Were Here (38), The Piper at the Gates of Dawn (163), Meddle (255), Animals (305), A Saucerful of Secrets (428), The Division Bell (719), A Momentary Lapse of Reason (789), and Atom Heart Mother (990). Barrett's The Madcap Laughs was No. 703.

- Billy Corgan inducted Pink Floyd into the Rock & Roll Hall of Fame in 1996 because he had always seen them as an inspiration. However, Roger Waters would continue to inspire Corgan in other ways. Billy's band Smashing Pumpkins was struggling after guitarist James Iha left the band. The band was reunited in 2018, and Corgan gave Roger Waters much of the credit. He said Roger had encouraged him to do so in a phone conversation. Also, Waters's solo work was in his mind. As he explained in a 2017 interview, "I have to say that Roger Waters, in talking to him personally and seeing him play live, particularly when I saw him do The Wall, has helped me to change my perception that there is an opportunity to re-contextualize my work in a way that imbues your work with a new energy while also satisfying the nostalgic revue."

CHAPTER 13:

INFLUENCE, LEGACY, AND MISCELLANY

TRIVIA TIME!

1. How many of Pink Floyd's five principal members (Barrett, Gilmour, Mason, Waters, and Wright) were born in 1944?

   a. Zero
   b. One
   c. Two
   d. Three

2. "It's hard to see why we were cast as the first British psychedelic group," a member of Pink Floyd said in 1968. "We never saw ourselves that way. We realized that we were, after all, only playing for fun, tied to no particular form of music." Who made that statement?

   a. Syd Barrett
   b. Nick Mason
   c. Roger Waters
   d. Rick Wright

3. True or False: Jeff Beck was briefly considered to replace Syd Barrett as Pink Floyd's lead guitarist in 1968.

4. Looking back on the early days of Pink Floyd, which member said, "Syd [Barrett] was a genius, but I wouldn't

want to go back to playing 'Interstellar Overdrive' for hours and hours"?

a. Rick Wright
b. Roger Waters
c. David Gilmour
d. Nick Mason

5. True or False: John Lennon and Yoko One appeared hand in hand at Pink Floyd's show during the legendary 14-Hour Technicolor Dream in London in 1967.

6. Which guitarist said he ran out and bought his first delay pedal after hearing the opening chords to "Dogs" from the *Animals* album?

a. Mike Campbell
b. Andy Summers
c. The Edge
d. Eddie Van Halen

7. Which Pink Floyd album became the first one to be played in outer space when Soviet cosmonauts brought it with them to the MIR space station in 1989?

a. *Wish You Were Here*
b. *The Dark Side of the Moon*
c. *The Wall*
d. *Delicate Sound of Thunder*

8. Which classic movie was rumored to synch up perfectly with *The Dark Side of the Moon*?

a. *Gone with the Wind*
b. *The Wizard of Oz*
c. *Citizen Kane*
d. *The Godfather*

9. Regarding the legal dispute, who said, "I don't think any of us came out of the years from 1985 with any credit"?

   a. David Gilmour
   b. Nick Mason
   c. Roger Waters
   d. Rick Wright

10. True or False: In 2016, the remastered version of Roger Waters's *Amused to Death* won the Grammy Award for the Best Surround Sound Album.

11. Which of the following bands did not explicitly mention Pink Floyd as one of its key influences?

   a. Radiohead
   b. Queen
   c. The Smashing Pumpkins
   d. The Clash

12. When Roger Waters was asked to identify the central theme of Pink Floyd's music, what was his answer?

   a. Alienation
   b. Empathy
   c. Mortality
   d. Truth

13. *Pink Floyd: Their Mortal Remains* is a multimedia exhibition covering the entire history of the band. Which song from *The Wall* is the phrase "mortal remains" taken from?

   a. "Goodbye Blue Sky"
   b. "Is There Anybody Out There?"
   c. "Nobody Home"
   d. "Goodbye Cruel World"

14. True or False: A giant inflatable flying pig hovered over the Victoria and Albert Museum to celebrate the opening of *Pink Floyd: Their Mortal Remains*.

15. Which of the following is <u>not</u> one of the artifacts displayed in the exhibition *Pink Floyd: Their Mortal Remains*?

    a. The actual wall from *The Wall – Live in Berlin*
    b. Syd Barrett's bicycle
    c. A page from Nick Mason's diary dated 1968
    d. A flower-petal shaped mirror ball used at concerts in the 1970s

16. Which city isscheduled to be the first US location to host *Pink Floyd: Their Mortal Remains*?

    a. Chicago
    b. Los Angeles
    c. New York
    d. Washington

17. The "Syd, Roger, Richard, Nick and David Playlist" launched on Spotify in 2020 with a live rendition of which classic Pink Floyd song?

    a. "Money"
    b. "Comfortably Numb"
    c. "Us and Them"
    d. "Another Brick in the Wall (Part 2)"

ANSWERS

1. a — Zero. Wright and Waters were born in 1943, Mason in 1945, Barrett and Gilmour in 1946.

2. d — Rick Wright

3. True — However, Beck says that no offer was extended. However, Richard Wright said in an interview that Beck turned the band down.

4. b — Roger Waters

5. False — Lennon and Ono were both there, but they didn't know each other yet.

6. c — The Edge

7. d — *Delicate Sound of Thunder*

8. b — *The Wizard of Oz*

9. c — Roger Waters

10. True

11. d — The Clash

12. b — Empathy

13. c — "Nobody Home"

14. True

15. a — The wall from *The Wall – Live in Berlin*

16. b — Los Angeles

17. c- Us and Them

DID YOU KNOW?

- Technological and creative innovations in sound effects and audio recording were a constant priority for Pink Floyd. The band used some of the earliest synthesizers and quadraphonic devices, upgrading each time that improved equipment became available. By the time of The Final Cut, Pink Floyd employed a Holophonic system that produced an effect of the sound moving around behind, above, left, or right of the listener.

- O'Neill Surber also pointed to absence or non-being as a key theme of Pink Floyd's work. For example, from "Jugband Blues": "I'm much obliged to you for making it clear that I'm not here." From "Comfortably Numb": "I cannot put my finger on it now; the child is grown, the dream is gone." Also, Waters said that Wish You Were Here was "about none of us really being there. It should've been called Wish We Were Here."

- The Wall originated with Roger Waters's literal desire to build a wall between the band and the audience at live performances. He had become increasingly disillusioned about the relationship between musicians (or celebrities in any field) and their fans. "Audiences at those vast concerts are there for an excitement which I think has to do with the love of success," said Waters. "When a band or a person becomes an idol, it can have to do with the success that that person manifests, not the quality of work he produces. You don't become a fanatic because somebody's work is good, you become a fanatic to be touched vicariously by their glamour and fame."

- In reviewing his career, Roger Waters said, "My view is that I've been involved in two absolutely classic albums — The Dark Side of the Moon and The Wall. And if you haven't got [Waters's solo album] Amused to Death, you haven't got the full set." He also described Amused to Death as "a stunning piece of work." Some critics agreed. For example, All Music called the album "a masterpiece in the sense that it brings together all of [Waters's] obsessions in one grand, but not unwieldy, package."

- Pink Floyd: Their Mortal Remains is a multimedia exhibition on the history of Pink Floyd. The exhibition includes audio, video, and a variety of artifacts lent by the band members and others associated with Pink Floyd. The exhibition opened at the Victoria and Albert Museum in London, running from May to October 2017 and attracting over 400,000 visitors. The exhibition has since been presented in Rome, Dortmund, and Madrid. It is scheduled to be presented in Los Angeles in 2021.

- In 2020, Pink Floyd launched the "Syd, Roger, Richard, Nick and David Playlist," available on Spotify and YouTube, with a live rendition of "Us and Them" recorded at the Empire Pool in London in 1974. The group planned to grow the list more or less constantly by adding classic tracks, deep cuts, and previously unavailable rarities from the 2011 Immersion box sets.

Printed in Great Britain
by Amazon